Part of
THE FLYING FISH

by

John Henry Gray

Illustrations designed by Peter Wormington and created primarily by ENROC ILLUSTRATION Co with individual drawings also by ANGEL MOSQUITO

First published 2016 by
Peter Wormington
Westfield, Bussage, Stroud, GL6 8BB.

Printed and bound by
Imago Printing.

Typeset by Mach 3 Solutions Limited, Bussge, GL6 8JY
www.mach3solutions.co.uk

ISBN 978-1-5262-0451-6

Part of
THE FLYING FISH

by

John Henry Gray

Of the birds that fly in the furthest sea,

six are more strange than others be.

Under its tumble, among the fish,

six are a marvel, passing wish.

First is a hawk, exceeding great,
he dwelleth alone, he hath no mate.

His neck is bound with a yellow ring;
on his breast is the crest of an ancient king.

The second bird is exceeding pale,
from little head to scanty tail.

She is striped with black on either wing,
which is rose-lined, like a costly thing.

Though small the bulk of the brilliant third,
of all blue birds, 'tis the bluest bird.

They fly in bands, and seen by day,
by the side of them the sky is grey.

I mind the fifth, I forget the fourth,
save that it comes from East and North.

The fifth is an orange
white billed duck;
he diveth for fish like
the god of Luck.

He hath never a foot
on which to stand,
for water yields, and
he loves not land.

This the end of many words, save one,
concerning marvellous birds.

The great faced dolphin is first of fish,
he is devil eyed and devilish.

Of all the fishes is he most brave;
he walks the sea like an angry wave.

The second, the fishes call their lord.
himself a bow, his face is a sword;

his sword is armed with a hundred teeth,
fifty above and fifty beneath.

The third has a suit of scarlet mail.

The fourth is naught but a feeble tail.

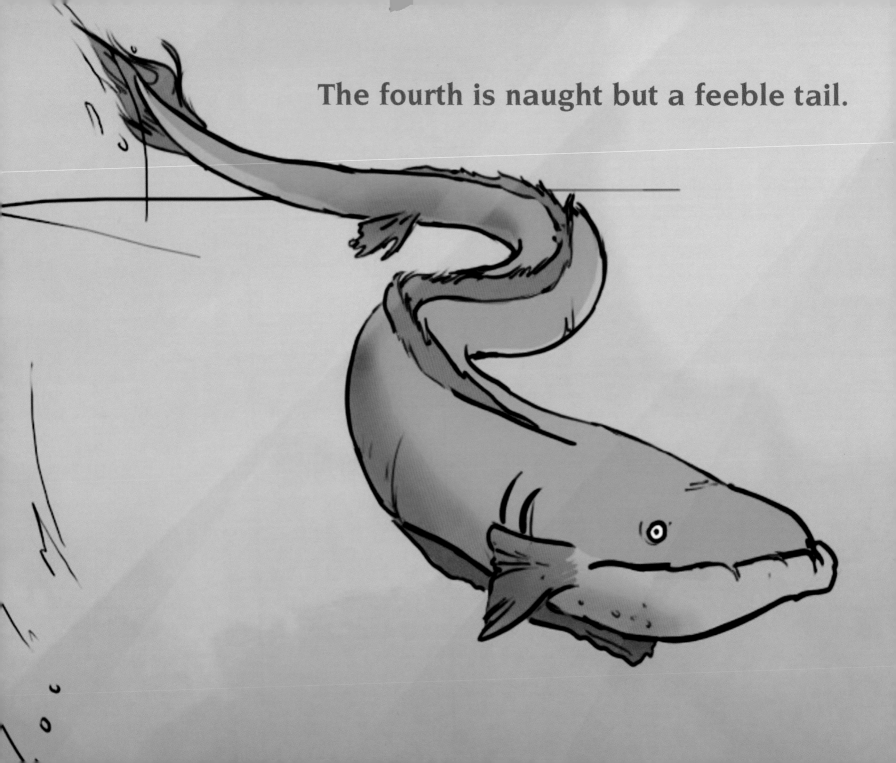

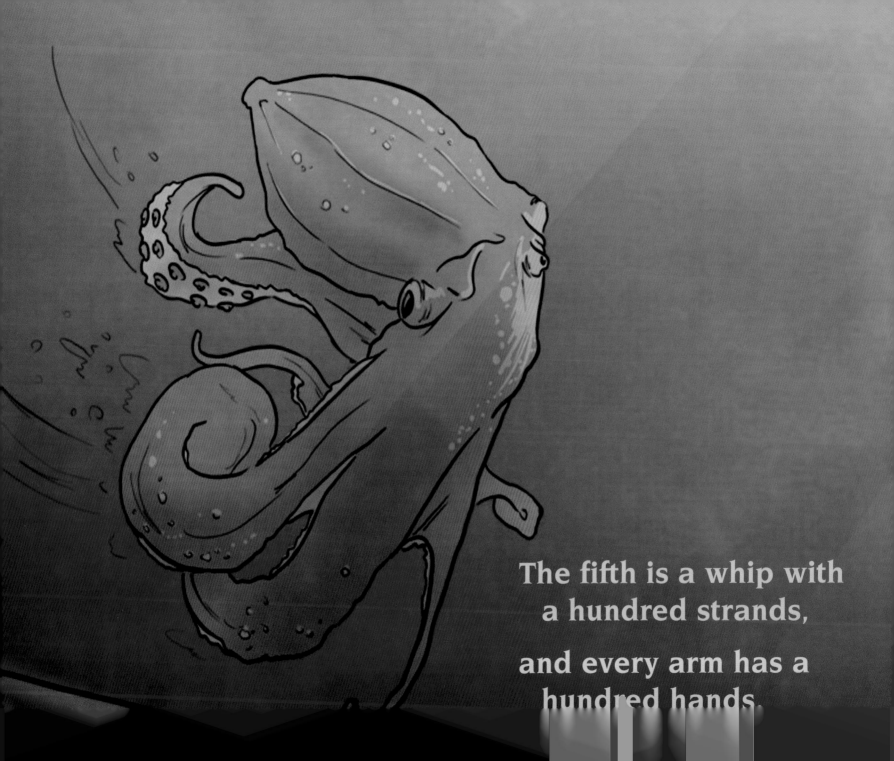

The fifth is a whip with a hundred strands, and every arm has a hundred hands.

The last strange fish is the last strange bird;
of him no sage hath even heard.

He roams the sea in a gleaming horde,
in fear of the dolphin and him of the sword.

He leaps from the sea with a silken swish,
he beats the air does the *Flying Fish*.

His eyes are round with excess of fright,
bright as the drops of his pinions flight.

In sea and sky he hath no peace,
for the five strange fish are
his enemies.

And the five strange fowls
keep watch for him,

they know him well by
his crystal gleam.

Oftwhiles, Sir Sage, on my junk's white deck, have I seen this fish bird come to wreck.

Oftwhiles, (fair deck) twixt bow and poop,
have I seen that piteous sky fish stoop.

His beauty passes
like bubbles flown
the white bright bird
is a fish of stone.

He pants in crystal and
mother of pearl,
while his body shrinks and
his pinions furl.

The bird so fair, for
its putrid sake,

is flung to the dogs
in the junks white wake.

Flying Fish

Flying Fish are found all over the world. They evolved to escape from the many fish that feed on them. Aerial flight gave them an enormous advantage over other small fish that were confined to the water. Some flying fish species developed one pair of wings, others two. They also developed stiffer skeletons to keep them rigid in flight. The average flight is around 50m at a height reaching 3m; but fish can sometimes fly 400m and reach a height of 10m with the help of the wind.

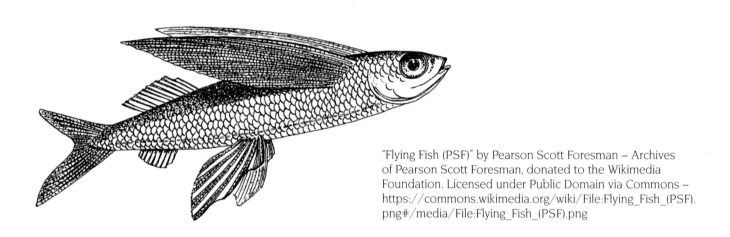

"Flying Fish (PSF)" by Pearson Scott Foresman – Archives of Pearson Scott Foresman, donated to the Wikimedia Foundation. Licensed under Public Domain via Commons – https://commons.wikimedia.org/wiki/File:Flying_Fish_(PSF). png#/media/File:Flying_Fish_(PSF).png

Flying fish spawn together in huge groups, with the females laying their sticky eggs on any floating object at the surface, while the males thrash about to fertilise the eggs. The floating objects get so heavy with hundreds of thousands of fertilized flying fish eggs that they will sink to the seabed, where the eggs eventually hatch.

Hundreds of thousands of dolphins also move close to shore in super-pods, chasing the shoals of flying fish and eating as many as they can. As the dolphins hunt the flying fish from below, the fish leap out the water in explosive, shiny squadrons that skim the water, glistening blue fins outstretched, often flying many metres to escape the chaos below.

Flying fish provide important seasonal fisheries for small-scale fishermen around the world, particularly in the Caribbean and Asia. In Sri Lanka the fishermen use the spectacle of the chasing dolphins and the flying fish squadrons to locate the huge shoals and set their nets.

The Marine Conservation Society (MCS) is the UK's leading charity for the protection of our seas, shores and wildlife. For over 30 years MCS has been the voice for the sea - for all the fascinating creatures that live beneath the waves, for our breathtaking coastal environment, for all those who make a sustainable living from the sea and for all those who simply enjoying visiting the beach and our glorious coastline.

We gain so much from our seas – food, energy, wellbeing and fun – yet our seas are suffering. MCS believes the key to safeguarding the health and prosperity of our seas is to promote change through active collaborative engagement with governments, people and businesses with the help of our many members, supporters and volunteers throughout the UK. Their work falls into the following key areas:

Marine wildlife protection

MCS works to protect our precious seas and wildlife by campaigning for marine protected areas in the UK, studying the amazing wildlife in our seas, and working on frontline conservation projects both in the UK and overseas.

Sustainable fisheries and seafood

MCS encourages everyone - shoppers, supermarkets, restaurants and caterers - to make more sustainable choices of seafood. Their popular **Good Fish Guide** has become the go-to resource for information on fish to eat, and fish to avoid.

Clean seas and beaches

Through their annual beach cleaning programme, MCS mobilises thousands of volunteers to pick up and record information on litter. This not only helps to clean up our coastline, but it also enables MCS to tackle the problems at source. Check out MCS's **Good Beach Guide** for full details of all the best beaches in the UK.

Get involved

You can help MCS to save our seas in many ways: by becoming a member of MCS; volunteering as a Sea Champion; fundraising; supporting their campaigns; or by signing up for their popular enewsletter.

For more information, go to: www.mcsuk.org

These kind people were particularly generous in helping this book to be published to support the work of the Marine Conservation Society (MCS)

Heather and Stephen Ayles
George and Catherine Campbell
Serena and John Campbell
Angie and Andrew Cash
J Michele Colenso
Caroline and Paul Crofts
Andrew and Moira French
Charles and Diane Gaskain
Alice Goodenough
Russell and Rebecca Gower
Jessica and Neil Granville
Nick Grono
Monika and Richard Grono
Will and Jane de Groot
Simon and Yvonne Hodges
Trish Holdway
Steve and Jocasta Keast
Hannah and Mathew Keyser

Penelope Kilbee
James Local
Thornton and Ann Maccallum
Pam and John Martin
Murdoch McAllister
Teresa and Matt Mockridge
William and Louisa Newlin
Catherine and Richard Nicholls
Robin and Ann Pearson
Adrian Pegg
Nick and Jo Penn
Rob and Palin Pilkington
Daniel Roberts
Andy and Eva Rozwadowski
Gursharan and Hardip Saini
Udam Saini
Sharon Shrivana Samaroo
Angad Singh

Suzanne Stogdon
James Staniland
Tiger and Debbie Timbs
Jan and David Vonberg
Natasha Walker and Uwe Krieger
Phillida Walker
William Walker
Jane Watson-Baker
Richard Winter
Paul and Caroline Wopshott
Polly and Ralph Wopshott
Estella Wormington
Hugh and Nicki Wormington
Jim and Jessie Wormington
Hilary and Keith Wright
Jonathan Wyatt
Patsy Davidson and Sandy Douglas

marine
conservation society